COMPREHENSION SKILLS

FACTS

LEVEL B

ESL Program

Linda Ward Beech

Tara McCarthy

Donna Townsend

STECK-VAUGHN
ELEMENTARY · SECONDARY · ADULT · LIBRARY

A Harcourt Company

www.steck-vaughn.com

Editorial Director:	Diane Schnell
Project Editor:	Anne Souby
Associate Director of Design:	Cynthia Ellis
Design Manager:	Cynthia Hannon
Media Researcher:	Christina Berry
Production:	Rusty Kay
Cover Illustration:	Stephanie Carter
Cover Production:	Alan Klemp
Photograph:	©PhotoDisc

ISBN 0-7398-2629-8

7 8 9 0   170   05 04

Facts are true things. Facts are things you can taste, touch, hear, smell, and see. In this book you will find facts in stories.

Facts are all around you. Trees grow tall. That is a fact. Water is wet. That is another fact. What facts can you see in this picture?

What Are Facts?

Facts are things you know are true. Everything you read has facts in it. Read this:

Bob was smiling. At last it was spring.

Bob was smiling. That is a fact. The time of year was spring. That is also a fact. There is one more fact you know. You know the person's name.

Try It!

Read this story. It has facts about what people used to think a long time ago.

The Earth and the Sun

Long ago a man was thinking about the sky. He had been watching the sun for days. He began to see it in a new way. "The Earth is going around the sun," he said. At that time most people thought the sun went around Earth. They thought Earth was the biggest and best thing in the sky.

The man said, "I must write a book. It might make people angry. But I must tell the truth." The man did write a book. But he never saw it printed. He died in 1543. The book was printed later that year.

People were angry when they read the book. They wanted to think that everything went around Earth. But today people know that the man was right.

How to Find Facts

Try to find the facts in the story. Write the facts on the lines below.

Fact 1: The man had been watching the _____ for days. (moon, Earth, sun)

Fact 2: The man died in the year _____. (1543, 1453, 1457)

Fact 3: The man said, "I must write a _____." (letter, story, book)

- ◆ To find facts you must know what to look for. For Fact 1 you must look for a thing the man watched. For Fact 2 you must look for a date. For Fact 3 you must look for what the man said. Read the story again. Draw a line under the words *sun*, *1543*, and *book*. They are the right answers for Facts 1, 2, and 3.

- ◆ To find the facts, read the story very carefully. If you cannot remember the facts, read the story again.

Practice Finding Facts

This book is filled with stories. After you read each story, you will answer some questions. The questions will ask about facts in the story.

Here is a story. Read it. Answer the questions.

◆
Remembering Things

What if you go to a store but forget your shopping list? You may not know what to buy. Here is a way to remember things without a list. Stand in a room in your home. Look at the things in the room. Then think of the things you need to buy. There may be a yellow chair in the room. It can help you remember bananas. A white pillow can help you remember milk. When you get to the store, think about the things in the room. You should be able to remember what to buy. You may even be able to go shopping without a list.

Now find some facts by answering the questions. The first one has been done for you.

__B__ **1.** To remember things without a list,
    A. go shopping
    B. stand in a room
    C. sit in a chair

_____ **2.** A white pillow can help you remember
    A. cookies
    B. butter
    C. milk

To check your answer, turn to page 60.

How to Use This Book

In this book there are 25 stories. Read the stories. Read the questions after the stories. Think about each question. Write the correct answer on the line.

You can check your answers yourself. If you wish, tear out pages 61 and 62. Find the unit you want to check. Fold the answer page on the dotted line to show the right unit. Write the number of answers you got right in the score box at the top of the page.

Remember

This book asks questions about facts in stories. You might know some other facts. But just use the facts in the stories to answer the questions.

Hints for Better Reading

◆ Read the questions carefully.
◆ Read the story again and again.

Challenge Yourself

Try this. Read a story. Cover it with a sheet of paper. Answer the questions without looking at the story.

Writing

On pages 30 and 58, there are stories with questions. These do not have answers for you to choose. Think of an answer. Write it in your own words. On pages 31 and 59, you are asked to write your own story. You are given a prewriting activity to help you. You will find suggested answers on page 60. But your answers may be very different.

Corn Foods of Mexico

Corn has been the main food of Mexico for a long time. Indians there learned to grow corn thousands of years ago. Today corn is still the chief food for most Mexicans.

Cornmeal is not hard to make. People first soften the corn in hot water. Then they boil the corn. Later they grind it into cornmeal.

In Mexico the main cornmeal food is the *tortilla*. It looks like a thin pancake. It is shaped by hand or machine. It is then cooked on a griddle.

_____ **1.** The main food of Mexico is
- **A.** water
- **B.** corn
- **C.** meat

_____ **2.** Indians in Mexico learned to grow corn
- **A.** thousands of years ago
- **B.** hundreds of years ago
- **C.** dozens of years ago

_____ **3.** People soften the corn in
- **A.** oil
- **B.** grease
- **C.** hot water

_____ **4.** In Mexico the main cornmeal food is a
- **A.** chicken
- **B.** tortilla
- **C.** cookie

Steck-Vaughn • Comprehension Skills Series

A tortilla may be eaten in different ways. It can be enjoyed just by itself. But it may also be eaten with other foods. Many Mexicans like to fold a tortilla in half. They fill it with chopped meat or cheese. Then they fry it. They've made a delicious taco!

Other people roll up a tortilla with the filling inside. Then they cover it with hot sauce. They've made a tasty enchilada! Mexicans also fry a flat tortilla to a crisp. They put beans, cheese, meat, lettuce, and onions on top. They've made a yummy tostada!

_____ **5.** A tortilla sometimes is eaten
  A. alone
  B. with bread
  C. with hot water

_____ **6.** A folded tortilla filled with meat or cheese is a
  A. tamale
  B. taco
  C. tostada

_____ **7.** An enchilada is rolled up and covered with
  A. hot sauce
  B. tomatoes
  C. pickles

_____ **8.** A tostada is very
  A. cold
  B. sour
  C. crisp

A Brave Bus Rider

Rosa Parks never planned to become famous. She grew up on a small farm in the South. Her family was poor. Rosa went to a school for black children. At the time blacks and whites could not go to the same schools. That was the law in the South.

Rosa later took a job. She rode the bus to work each day. Black people had to sit in the back of the bus. Sometimes many white riders got on. Then black riders had to give up their seats to them. It was a law in her city.

_____ **1.** Rosa Parks grew up
- **A.** on a small farm
- **B.** in a big city
- **C.** in a large school

_____ **2.** Rosa went to a school
- **A.** for white children
- **B.** for black children
- **C.** for all children

_____ **3.** Black people on the bus sat
- **A.** in the front
- **B.** in the back
- **C.** in the middle

_____ **4.** Blacks had to give up their seats because
- **A.** whites walked to work
- **B.** the seats were broken
- **C.** it was the law

One evening in 1955, Rosa left work. She was very tired. She got on the bus to go home. Soon a white rider needed her seat. Rosa was told to move. Rosa refused. The driver called the police. Rosa was taken to jail.

That week the city's black leaders made a plan. No blacks would ride the bus to work. They would walk or go by car. The plan worked for more than a year. The bus company lost lots of money. At last the city changed its laws. Later new laws were made for the whole country. Rosa Parks was known all over the world for her bravery!

_____ **5.** When Rosa was told to move, she
   A. said no
   B. agreed to do it
   C. shared her seat

_____ **6.** Blacks decided
   A. to ride in the front of the bus
   B. not to ride the bus
   C. to ride their own buses

_____ **7.** Their plan went on for
   A. more than a year
   B. less than a year
   C. more than two years

_____ **8.** The city finally
   A. ran fewer buses
   B. shut down all buses
   C. changed its laws

Seashells

Seashells come in many different shapes, sizes, and colors. Some shells grow as big as four feet long. Some shells are smaller than half an inch long. Some shells have two sides that open like wings. Other shells are shaped like a curling tube. Shells come in all colors: white, black, brown, yellow, green, red, orange, and pink. They are like a rainbow in the ocean.

Many seashells are named for other things we know. The spider shell is one example. The spider shell has long points that look like spider legs. The comb shell has points, too. Its points are straight and close together, just like those in a comb.

_____ 1. Some shells grow
- A. rainbows
- B. four feet long
- C. butterfly wings

_____ 2. The smallest shells are
- A. half a foot long
- B. two inches wide
- C. smaller than half an inch long

_____ 3. Some shells are named for
- A. people who found them
- B. other things we know
- C. where they are found

_____ 4. Some seashells have
- A. arms
- B. points
- C. homes

$$\bigcirc$$

There are two kinds of bear shells. One is called the little bear. It is a small shell. The bear-paw shell is different. It is a big shell with two parts. Each half looks like an animal foot.

Some names of shells do not make any sense. The apple shell doesn't look like an apple at all. And the dog shell doesn't look like a dog. The butterfly shell is very plain. Many other shells look more like a butterfly than that one! But the heart shell does have the shape of a heart. Not all heart shells are red. Some are yellow. Others have brown spots.

_____ **5.** There are
  A. two kinds of bear shells
  B. three types of butterflies
  C. two kinds of apple shells

_____ **6.** The bear-paw shell has
  A. one part
  B. two parts
  C. three parts

_____ **7.** The dog shell
  A. looks like an animal foot
  B. doesn't look like a dog
  C. is yellow or red

_____ **8.** Sometimes the heart shell has
  A. brown spots
  B. a butterfly shape
  C. three points

UNIT 4

A Cowboy's Life

Did you ever see an old TV show or movie about cowboys? It made their life seem fun and exciting all the time. But a real cowboy's life was mainly hard work. Most cowboys worked on a ranch. They had to keep an eye on cows in the herd. Sometimes cows tried to run away. Cowboys had to chase them down and bring them back.

Many cows were sold to buyers far away. So cowboys went on trail drives. They led the cows to the buyers in other towns. The trail could be 1,000 miles or more. A trail drive could last two or three months.

_____ **1.** A TV show makes a cowboy's life seem
  A. hard
  B. fun
  C. long

_____ **2.** Most real cowboys worked on a
  A. ranch
  B. farm
  C. home

_____ **3.** A cowboy kept an eye mostly on
  A. fires
  B. horses
  C. cows

_____ **4.** A trail drive could last
  A. two years
  B. two or three months
  C. one day

Cowboys needed good, strong horses. They rode them all day long. Sometimes they rode part of the night, too. The horses were called "cow ponies." They had to be fast and smart. They had to sense a cow's every move. The horses worked as hard as their riders did!

Cowboys also wore special clothing. Their hats had wide brims. This kept sun and rain off their faces. They also used hats to scoop water from a stream. Cowboys wore vests instead of coats. These had pockets to hold coins or a watch. Cowboys also wore tall, rugged boots for long rides.

_____ **5.** Cowboys rode their horses
   A. all day
   B. once a week
   C. every other day

_____ **6.** A horse had to sense
   A. when other horses were near
   B. when a rider was tired
   C. what a cow might do next

_____ **7.** A cowboy hat had a wide brim to
   A. put coins in
   B. keep the hat on tighter
   C. protect the cowboy's face

_____ **8.** While riding, cowboys wore
   A. sneakers
   B. moccasins
   C. high boots

Saving the Animals

A river had been blocked to make a lake. At first the water came up slowly. The animals must have thought it was the spring rains. But soon all the valleys were under water. The hills looked like islands. And all the animals were gathered on those islands. They were trapped!

Some people wanted to save the animals. There were thousands of animals to save. The people had to hurry. Before long the water would cover the little islands. The people quickly found nets to catch the animals. Then they got boats to travel in. Soon they were ready.

_____ **1.** The hills looked like
   A. elephants
   B. islands
   C. rivers

_____ **2.** The animals were
   A. hungry
   B. lost
   C. trapped

_____ **3.** The people had to
   A. walk quietly
   B. get money
   C. hurry

_____ **4.** To catch the animals, people found
   A. cages
   B. nets
   C. sacks

The people went out to the islands. There were many different kinds of deer there. The deer were more afraid of the people than of the water. They would kick to get away. The people had to cover the deer's eyes. Then the deer would be still.

Besides the deer there were wild pigs. They were hard to catch because they could run so fast. The monkeys were also hard to catch. They would chatter loudly and climb the trees. When an animal was caught, it was carefully tied up. The people took the animals across the new lake to land. The animals were sent to animal parks where they would be safe.

_____ **5.** The deer would
  A. kick to get away
  B. chatter loudly
  C. bite and scratch

_____ **6.** The wild pigs
  A. were easy to catch
  B. jumped into the water
  C. could run very fast

_____ **7.** When they caught the animals, the people
  A. put them in cages
  B. gave them food
  C. tied them up

_____ **8.** The animals were taken to
  A. animal parks
  B. a circus
  C. another island

Old Glass Bottles

Glass bottles were first made about three thousand years ago. The oldest bottles were made by hand. People blew them into different shapes. Long iron tubes were used to blow the glass. People dipped the tubes into melted glass. Then they blew through the tubes. Finally they broke the bottles off the tubes. The tubes left a mark on the finished glass. This mark shows that the glass was blown.

There are other ways to tell if a bottle was made by hand. The glass might have bubbles in it. The bubbles probably came from boiling the glass. Many times the bubbles would stay in the glass as it cooled.

_____ **1.** Glass bottles were first made
  A. three thousand years ago
  B. four hundred years ago
  C. one thousand years ago

_____ **2.** People made the oldest bottles
  A. out of wood
  B. with machines
  C. by hand

_____ **3.** To blow the glass, people used
  A. glass pots
  B. old bottles
  C. iron tubes

_____ **4.** Bubbles might come from
  A. soap
  B. breaking the glass
  C. boiling the glass

Then people began making glass bottles other ways. They made bottles by pouring the glass into forms. It took two forms to make a bottle. There was one form for each half. Bottles made this way have lines down the sides. That's where the two halves were joined together.

Some old bottles have letters written in the glass. The letters are on the side or the bottom. You can feel them because they stick out. These letters tell the name of the bottle company. There are books that tell about the different companies. The books tell you when and where each bottle was made.

_____ **5.** People used other ways to
      A. make bottles
      B. blow glass
      C. write letters

_____ **6.** Bottles with lines down the sides were
      A. blown with a new kind of tool
      B. broken and then fixed
      C. poured into two forms

_____ **7.** Some bottles have letters on the
      A. inside of the bottle
      B. side or bottom
      C. top of the bottle

_____ **8.** To find out when a bottle was made,
      A. use a book that tells about bottle companies
      B. learn to blow glass
      C. count the lines on the side of the glass

UNIT 7

Liz's Adventure

"What a great day for a walk!" Liz said. She could hear the birds singing. It was a good morning for adventure. After breakfast Liz took off. She whistled a tune as she walked. She followed a trail up the mountain. She walked for a while, and then she looked for a rock to rest on. Liz was tired. "What a mountain climber I turned out to be!" she said.

While she rested, Liz looked around. Suddenly she saw the opening to a cave. It was big enough to walk through. "I wonder how deep this cave is," she said to herself. "Maybe there are cave drawings inside! I guess the only way to find out is to see for myself."

_____ **1.** Liz could hear
   A. running water
   B. mountain lions
   C. birds singing

_____ **2.** As she walked on the trail, Liz
   A. picked flowers
   B. whistled a tune
   C. sang a song

_____ **3.** After a while Liz felt
   A. hungry
   B. tired
   C. angry

_____ **4.** The opening to the cave was
   A. big enough to walk through
   B. full of water
   C. covered by a dead tree

18

At first Liz had no trouble seeing in the cave. She went around a bend. Then she lit a match. "Just a little farther," she said to herself. Suddenly her match went out. She lit another one. But now things looked strange.

When her second match went out, Liz became really frightened. She thought she heard a scratching noise. Liz struck her last match. In the light she saw hundreds of bats hanging on to the top of the cave. They were hanging upside down. Liz backed up and ran out of the cave as fast as she could. She did not want to scare the bats. She knew that they needed their rest before they flew out at night to catch insects. Liz was happy. She had found a bat cave!

_____ **5.** When the second match went out, Liz
- **A.** started laughing
- **B.** stopped running
- **C.** became frightened

_____ **6.** Liz heard a noise that sounded like
- **A.** screaming
- **B.** breathing
- **C.** scratching

_____ **7.** Liz saw hundreds of bats
- **A.** hanging on to the top of the cave
- **B.** resting on the floor
- **C.** fighting with each other

_____ **8.** The bats flew
- **A.** at Liz
- **B.** to the match
- **C.** at night

Good Foods, Poor Names

1 Some foods have names that make good sense. Take an orange, for example. Its color is orange. So it seems only right to call the fruit by that name.

2 But what about the peanut? True, it is a kind of pea. Like other peas, a peanut grows in a shell, or pod. But a peanut is not a nut. It might seem like a nut. After all, it is small, round, and hard. But a peanut is not part of the nut family. So the name *peanut* is really not the best name for the food! Can you think of a better name for the peanut?

_____ **1.** An orange gets its name because
   A. it is a round fruit
   B. it is juicy inside
   C. its color is orange

_____ **2.** A peanut is a kind of
   A. pea
   B. nut
   C. pea and nut

_____ **3.** A peanut grows in a
   A. shell
   B. pit
   C. skin

_____ **4.** A peanut is
   A. long and soft
   B. small and round
   C. flat and square

3 Did you ever eat a pineapple? You may have liked its taste. But how good is its name? A pineapple is neither a pine nor an apple. It looks like a large pine cone. But it is not in the pine family. It is not in the apple family, either. What might be a better name for a pineapple?

4 You might enjoy grapefruit. But its name is not the best. Yes, it is a fruit. But it is not in the grape family. Grapes grow on vines. Grapefruit grow on trees. What does all this prove? The names of foods can be food for thought!

_____ **5.** A pineapple is
    A. both a pine and an apple
    B. not a pine or an apple
    C. a pine but not an apple

_____ **6.** A pineapple looks like
    A. a big pine cone
    B. a big apple
    C. a big grape

_____ **7.** A grapefruit is
    A. a grape but not a fruit
    B. both a grape and a fruit
    C. a fruit but not a grape

_____ **8.** Grapefruit grow on
    A. vines
    B. trees
    C. pines

Our Amazing Skin

Our skin is like a bag that we live in. Inside the bag our bodies are mostly water. Our water is like the water in the sea. It is very salty. Also, like the ocean, we can lose our water. The wind and the sun could take it away. Our bag of skin keeps our body's ocean from drying up.

Our skin keeps out sunshine. Too much sun can hurt us. Skin also keeps out dirt. That's important because some kinds of dirt can make us sick. Our skin feels things. It feels warm things, cold things, things it touches, and things that hurt it. A campfire feels warm. A snowball thrown in our face feels cold and hurts. A hug is the touch of another person's skin on our own.

_____ **1.** Our bodies are mostly
  A. salt
  B. water
  C. skin

_____ **2.** Our skin keeps our body's water from
  A. drying up
  B. getting cold
  C. smelling bad

_____ **3.** Skin keeps out
  A. dirt
  B. food
  C. water

_____ **4.** Our skin helps us
  A. read
  B. feel
  C. dream

Our hair is a special kind of covering. It helps keep things out of our eyes, ears, and nose. Hair is also good for keeping us warm. When we get goose bumps, our body hairs stand up. Then the hairs hold air close to our skin like a thin blanket. Hair keeps animals warm, too. Some animals have more hair than others. So they have a better blanket for cold weather.

Our nails are like very hard skin. They help keep our fingers and toes from getting hurt. Our nails aren't as strong or sharp as the nails that animals have. But they are good for scratching backs and picking up coins.

_____ **5.** Hair helps keep things out of our
      A. fingers and toes
      B. mouth and ears
      C. eyes, ears, and nose

_____ **6.** Hair is good for
      A. keeping us clean
      B. helping us stay warm
      C. keeping us from getting hurt

_____ **7.** Nails are like
      A. flat hair
      B. hard skin
      C. thin blankets

_____ **8.** Nails help keep our
      A. toes sharp
      B. fingers from getting loose
      C. toes from getting hurt

Silver Wings

During World War II, many of the men had to go fight. The women of the United States had to do the work the men had done.

One woman started a women's air force. It was called the Women's Air Force Service Pilots. It became known as the WASPs. To join the WASPs, a woman had to know how to fly. Then she had to go to flying school for six months to learn more. The WASPs learned to fly at night. They learned how to find their way on a long trip. The flying school was very hard. One out of three women did not pass the tests.

_____ **1.** During the war women had to
  A. do work the men had done
  B. go fight
  C. do nothing

_____ **2.** WASPs was the name of
  A. a special airplane
  B. the flying school
  C. an all-woman air force

_____ **3.** To join the WASPs, a woman had to
  A. know how to fly
  B. jump out of airplanes
  C. be a fast learner

_____ **4.** The WASPs went to a flying school for
  A. six months
  B. twelve years
  C. two days a week

The women who did pass got their silver wings. That means that they became pilots. More than one thousand women passed. Most WASPs flew new planes. They moved planes from one place to another place as the war changed. Some women had to test planes after they had been repaired. Flying was not always safe. Several of the pilots died.

The women's air force lasted just two years. But these women had done much in those two years. They had flown more than twelve thousand planes to the war.

_____ **5.** The WASPs who passed got
   A. silver stars
   B. a gold chain
   C. silver wings

_____ **6.** The number of women who passed was
   A. two
   B. twelve thousand
   C. one thousand

_____ **7.** The WASPs lasted
   A. six weeks
   B. two years
   C. three months

_____ **8.** In the end the WASPs
   A. moved twelve thousand planes
   B. all died in the war
   C. stayed in the air force

The Greatest Wall

Do you know the longest wall ever built? It is the Great Wall of China. It is nearly 4,000 miles long. Workers began to build the wall about 2,400 years ago. The job took 2,000 years to finish. Most of the wall still stands today.

The Chinese put up the wall to keep out enemies. The task was long and slow. The whole wall was made by hand. Workers used stones and bricks for most of the job. They made the wall 25 feet high. They made the base 25 feet wide. Towers sit along the top of the wall. Guards once stood in them to watch over the land.

_____ **1.** The Great Wall of China is
   A. nearly 2,400 miles long
   B. about 2,000 miles long
   C. nearly 4,000 miles long

_____ **2.** The job of building the wall took
   A. 2,000 years
   B. 2,400 years
   C. 4,000 years

_____ **3.** China put up the wall
   A. to scare other countries
   B. to give workers jobs
   C. to keep out enemies

_____ **4.** Workers built most of the wall with
   A. large machines
   B. stones and bricks
   C. old steel

One part of the wall was hardest to build. That part runs through land with hills and deserts. Bricks and stones were hard to find there. So workers used earth to build that part of the wall. First they made the earth wet. Then they pounded it to make it hard.

The wall did its job for small attacks. But for big ones, it did not work well. In the 1200s Genghis Khan marched into China and took over the land. The wall did not keep his troops out. Today the wall no longer is used to protect China. But visitors come from all over to see it.

_____ **5.** The wall was hardest to build
    A. over rivers and streams
    B. in hills and deserts
    C. through forests

_____ **6.** Workers built with earth by
    A. wetting and pounding it
    B. mixing it with brick
    C. mixing it with stone

_____ **7.** The wall was no help in
    A. small attacks
    B. big attacks
    C. any attacks

_____ **8.** Today the wall
    A. is visited by many people
    B. still protects China
    C. has mostly fallen

Two of Everything

Long ago in a land far away, there lived a man and his wife. They had a tiny house with a tiny garden. They were poor, but they were happy.

One afternoon the man was digging in the garden. He found a strange-looking pot. He called to his wife. She came over and looked inside. Her cap fell into the pot. She reached in to get it. To her surprise, she found her cap plus another one just like it. The man was curious. He dropped in a coin. He reached in to get it. To his surprise, he found his coin plus another one just like it.

_____ **1.** The man and wife owned a
    A. large home
    B. tiny house
    C. new car

_____ **2.** The man found a strange-looking
    A. pot
    B. cap
    C. coin

_____ **3.** In the pot the wife found
    A. her cap plus two coins
    B. her cap plus another one just like it
    C. nothing at all

_____ **4.** The man dropped a coin in the pot because he
    A. was careless
    B. was curious
    C. wanted to make a wish

"This is amazing!" the man shouted. "This pot makes two of everything! Let's put in more!" He put in a cup of water, and out came two cups. His wife put in a potato, and out came two potatoes.

"Let's put in our kitchen table!" shouted the wife. The couple took the table and tried to push it into the pot. The table was too big. The couple pushed very hard. The pot finally broke in two.

"Oh, well," the man sighed. "We were happy before having the pot. And we can still be happy now." And so they were!

_____ **5.** The man discovered that the pot
   A. had no bottom
   B. was very heavy
   C. made two of everything

_____ **6.** When the woman put in a potato,
   A. two potatoes came out
   B. the potato was cooked
   C. the potato disappeared

_____ **7.** The table was
   A. too small for the pot
   B. too large for the pot
   C. just right for the pot

_____ **8.** After breaking the pot, the couple still were
   A. happy
   B. sad
   C. puzzled

Writing

Read the story below. Think about the facts. Then answer the questions in complete sentences.

> Today we know many facts about the moon. Humans have traveled to the moon and back. They have brought back soil to study.
>
> The moon's soil is made of rock and glass. Some of the rock is small and ground up. Other rock is in large chunks. The glass on the moon is very tiny. Each bit is about as small as the period at the end of this sentence. In the future more trips to the moon will be made. Then we will learn even more facts about its soil.

1. How do we know facts about the moon today?

_____

_____

2. What is the moon's soil made of?

_____

_____

3. How small is the glass on the moon?

_____

_____

To check your answers, turn to page 60.

Prewriting

Think of an idea you might write about, such as a place you visited or an item you found. Write the idea in the center of the idea web below. Then fill out the rest of the web with facts.

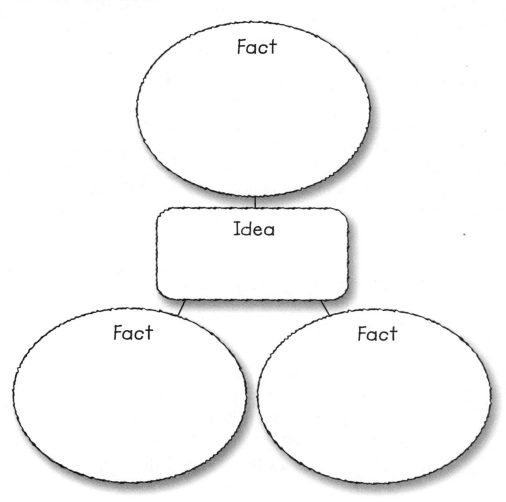

On Your Own

Now use another sheet of paper to write a story about your idea. Use the facts from your idea web.

To check your answers, turn to page 60.

Crazy Town, U.S.A.

Towns get their names in many ways. One town in Wyoming is called Ten Sleep. People there had their own way of telling how far away a place was. They would tell how many nights one had to sleep on a trip there. This town was ten nights from three other places.

Ong's Hat, New Jersey, got its name in a funny way. A man named Jacob Ong lived in this village. He liked three things: dancing, women, and his fancy hat. One night he was at a big dance. One woman thought that he should dance with her more. Finally she grabbed his fancy hat and threw it on the floor. Then she danced all over his hat.

_____ **1.** One town in Wyoming is called
   A. Three Sheep
   B. Ong's Hat
   C. Ten Sleep

_____ **2.** Ten Sleep got its name from the
   A. name of a man who lived there
   B. way people told how far to travel
   C. river that ran through the town

_____ **3.** Jacob Ong had a village named after his
   A. dance
   B. hat
   C. mother

_____ **4.** Ong got into trouble when he was
   A. at a big dance
   B. telling a funny story
   C. talking to a man

In New Mexico there is a place called Pie Town. A man started making little fruit pies to sell at his gas station. Then the people who owned the food store got the same idea. They started selling big pies. One day a cowboy passed through town. He said, "This sure is a pie town." Pie Town became the new name.

Midnight, Mississippi, got its name from a card game. The farmers would get together to play cards. Late one night a player lost all his money. Then he bet his land. But he lost that, too. The winner looked at his watch. "It's midnight," he said. "That's what I'll call my new land!"

_____ **5.** A man sold fruit pies at his
   A. friend's house
   B. pie shop
   C. gas station

_____ **6.** Pie Town was named by
   A. a cowboy who passed through
   B. the owner of the gas station
   C. the state of New Mexico

_____ **7.** In Mississippi the farmers would
   A. make pies and sell them
   B. work for many days and nights
   C. get together to play cards

_____ **8.** The winner of the card game
   A. named his land Pie Town
   B. won at twelve o'clock
   C. lived in Alaska

Animal Tracks

Animal tracks can tell you many things. For example, most cat tracks are smaller than dog tracks. Also, cat tracks are more rounded than dog tracks are. Cats usually keep their nails pulled in, but dogs can't do that. So dog tracks show nail marks.

Horse, deer, and goat tracks are different, too. Horses have one toe. A horse's foot is like a big toenail. It leaves tracks that look like a U. But deer and goats have two toes. Their feet are split into two parts. They leave tracks that look more like a V. If these animals are walking, their tracks are evenly spaced. But if they are running, their tracks are bunched together.

_____ **1.** Cat tracks
   A. are longer than dog tracks
   B. look smaller than dog tracks
   C. have more nail marks

_____ **2.** Dog prints
   A. have nail marks
   B. are round
   C. have a large heel

_____ **3.** A horse's foot
   A. is like a big toenail
   B. leaves no tracks
   C. is split into two parts

_____ **4.** Goat tracks are shaped like a
   A. W
   B. U
   C. V

Steck-Vaughn • Comprehension Skills Series

Rabbits have small, round front feet. Their back feet are big and long. But their tracks look funny. The prints of the two front feet are behind the prints of the two back feet. When rabbits hop, they land with their back feet in front of the place where their front feet were.

Birds leave tracks that look like scratch marks. They have four toes. Big birds walk just the way people do. Their tracks show first one foot, then the other foot. Small birds hop. Their tracks show two feet beside each other. Birds that swim leave different tracks. They have skin between their toes to help them swim. When these birds walk on land, that skin leaves a small print.

_____ **5.** Rabbits' back feet are
  A. big and long
  B. round and big
  C. small and long

_____ **6.** When rabbits hop,
  A. their ears flop down
  B. they move very slowly
  C. their back feet land in the front

_____ **7.** Big birds leave tracks that show
  A. three toes that look like scratch marks
  B. first one foot, then the other foot
  C. skin between their toes

_____ **8.** Small birds
  A. can only hop
  B. have skin between their toes
  C. walk the way people do

An Amazing Life

Helen Keller became ill while she was still a baby. The illness caused her to lose her sight and hearing. Because she could not see or hear, she did not know how to speak. Helen was shut off from the rest of the world.

At age 7 Helen was given a private teacher. Her name was Anne Sullivan. Anne was nearly blind as a child. She knew how it felt not to see. Anne taught Helen through touch. She spelled out letters on Helen's hand. The letters spelled the names of things. Anne placed those things in Helen's hand. Soon Helen knew how to spell words.

_____ **1.** Helen's illness caused her to
    A. lose her taste
    B. lose her touch
    C. lose her sight and hearing

_____ **2.** As a child, Helen
    A. could only whisper
    B. spoke normally
    C. was not able to speak

_____ **3.** Anne Sullivan taught Helen
    A. by phone
    B. through music
    C. through touch

_____ **4.** Anne spelled letters on Helen's
    A. throat
    B. hand
    C. eyes

Helen wanted to learn more. At age 10 she began to learn to speak. Her teacher spoke to her. Helen placed a finger on the speaker's lips and throat. By age 16 Helen could speak pretty well. She went to college and made top grades.

After college Helen worked to help other people who were blind. She taught them to have hope and to be brave. She wrote many books about her life. She gave speeches all over the world. She raised lots of money for those who were blind. Helen Keller became a hero to people everywhere.

_____ **5.** At age 10 Helen started to learn
      A. to talk
      B. to sing
      C. to write

_____ **6.** Helen felt a speaker's
      A. nose and ears
      B. eyes and hands
      C. throat and lips

_____ **7.** Helen wrote books about
      A. famous people
      B. her own life
      C. how the brain works

_____ **8.** Helen helped people who were blind by
      A. raising money for them
      B. letting Anne teach them
      C. becoming a doctor

Keeping Time

The first people had no way to measure time. They knew that the sun came up and went down. They knew that sometimes it was hot and sometimes it was cold. But they did not know about days, weeks, or months. People probably thought of days first. The sun went down, and then it came up again every morning. Later, people thought of months when they watched the moon.

One early calendar had 12 months. Each month had 30 days. But the people had made a mistake. If each month had 30 days, then there would be 5 days left over when the year ended. At last people fixed the calendar. They added 5 more days to the year.

_____ **1.** The first people
   A. lived in cold areas
   B. couldn't see the sun
   C. had no way to measure time

_____ **2.** People might have first thought of
   A. days
   B. months
   C. years

_____ **3.** One of the first calendars had
   A. 5 days
   B. 30 days
   C. 12 months

_____ **4.** To fix the calendar, people had to
   A. add 5 more days to the year
   B. match the months and the seasons
   C. add 1 day every 5 years

People first used the sun to tell time. A stick was put in the middle of a ring of rocks. The stick's shadow would move from rock to rock. But this clock wouldn't work on cloudy days. It wouldn't work at night or inside.

So people came up with new kinds of clocks. Some of these clocks burned. One kind was made from a rope. Another kind was made from a candle. The people drew lines on these clocks. They knew that it took about an hour to burn down to each line. Then someone had the idea of using sand in a clock. The sand ran slowly through a hole. The sand clock is still used today. We call it an hourglass.

_____ **5.** People first
  A. put sand in clocks
  B. used the sun to tell time
  C. made clocks from candles

_____ **6.** The first clocks didn't work
  A. in the sun
  B. at night
  C. without clouds

_____ **7.** The burning clocks were made from
  A. candles and ropes
  B. sand and candles
  C. candles and wood

_____ **8.** The hourglass is a
  A. burning clock
  B. water clock
  C. sand clock

A Farm Surprise

Amy lived in a big city. But she spent each summer on her grandparents' farm in the country. There she helped with the work. Often she took long walks with the farm dog, Shep. Amy liked her summers on the farm.

"Today you will learn something new. It's a surprise," her grandpa said with a smile. Grandma smiled, too.

Amy walked with her grandfather in the cool, gray morning. The sun was just coming up in the east. Shep ran through the green grass sparkling with dew. Amy helped her grandpa feed the cows in the barn.

_____ **1.** Amy lived
    A. by the sea
    B. in a big city
    C. on a train

_____ **2.** Amy's grandparents worked
    A. on a railroad
    B. in a store
    C. on a farm

_____ **3.** Amy visited the farm in the
    A. winter
    B. summer
    C. fall

_____ **4.** The farm dog was called
    A. Shep
    B. Amy
    C. Sam

Amy and her grandpa went back in the house. There Grandma had a big pitcher of cold milk. Thick, yellow cream was on top of the milk. Grandma poured the milk and cream into a large bottle. Then she put on the lid. The lid had a handle and paddles hooked to it. The paddles splashed in the milk.

"This is the surprise," said Grandma. "It's a butter churn. You turn the handle, and the cream sticks to the paddles. Then you take the paddles out and scrape off the cream. You put it in a bowl and add some salt, and you have butter." After turning the handle, Amy helped to eat the sweet butter on fresh bread.

_____ **5.** Grandma had a pitcher of
    A. water
    B. tea
    C. milk

_____ **6.** The surprise was a
    A. butter churn
    B. new dog
    C. birthday cake

_____ **7.** The cream stuck to the
    A. handle
    B. paddles
    C. barn

_____ **8.** Butter is made from
    A. ice
    B. pigs
    C. cream

Daydream

A fly buzzed around the classroom. Tom was supposed to be reading his book, but every few minutes his eyes would cross. Then he would find himself watching the fly as it went round and round and round the room.

Then Tom thought he heard a whisper. He couldn't believe it, but the fly was talking to him! "Hey, Tom, listen. I'm over here, Tom. Do you want to go for a ride? Hop on!" Suddenly Tom was riding on the fly's back! He held onto some of the hairs growing there. They were as thick as rope. The fly's big eyes looked beautiful. They had many changing colors, like a soap bubble.

_____ **1.** Tom was
    A. talking to the teacher
    B. doing his homework
    C. watching the fly

_____ **2.** Tom thought he heard a
    A. bee
    B. shout
    C. whisper

_____ **3.** Tom held onto the fly's
    A. hairs
    B. legs
    C. wings

_____ **4.** The fly's eyes
    A. opened and closed quickly
    B. were very small
    C. looked like a soap bubble

The fly went around the room. Tom looked down at the children in his class. They were all reading. He looked down at Mrs. Mott, his teacher. How strange people looked from above! Their noses looked too big. Sue's hair wasn't parted straight, and Frank's ears looked like handles on a sugar bowl. Just then Tom heard a voice.

"Tom! Tom, wake up! You'll have to stay after school today. You didn't finish your reading, young man," said Mrs. Mott. "Oh. Uh, yes, ma'am," Tom said. He looked up and saw the fly still buzzing in the corner.

_____ **5.** Mrs. Mott was Tom's
     A. mother
     B. teacher
     C. aunt

_____ **6.** Tom noticed that Sue's
     A. book was open
     B. answers were not right
     C. part was not straight

_____ **7.** Frank's ears looked
     A. smaller than pennies
     B. just like Sue's ears
     C. like handles on a sugar bowl

_____ **8.** Tom heard
     A. a voice
     B. cars honking
     C. a bell ring

Bicycles

People who rode the first bicycles worked hard. They had to push their feet against the ground to make their bikes move. These bikes, called hobby horses, had four wheels.

Later, people began to make bikes with two wheels. But the bikes were not like those seen on the streets today. People sat above the front wheel of the bikes. As they rode, their feet turned the wheel. Bicycle makers tried making big front wheels and small front wheels. They learned that bikes with larger front wheels could move faster. So they started making bikes with large front wheels and small back wheels.

_____ **1.** Hobby horses had
    A. big wheels
    B. two wheels
    C. four wheels

_____ **2.** On later bikes people
    A. sat above the front wheel
    B. pushed their feet against the ground
    C. rode a long way without stopping

_____ **3.** Bicycle makers tried making
    A. no wheels at all
    B. small front wheels
    C. rubber wheels

_____ **4.** Bikes with larger front wheels were
    A. slower
    B. faster
    C. safer

Soon the streets were filled with bikes with huge front wheels. Some bikes had wheels that were five feet tall. Many people were hurt when they fell off these bikes.

Later, people in England made a bike with smaller wheels. The two wheels on the new bike were almost the same size. People sat between the wheels, and their feet pushed two pedals. The two pedals moved a chain that turned the back wheel. The new bike was called a safety bike. People could ride on it without falling five feet to the ground. This safe bike became the model for today's bikes.

_____ **5.** The streets were filled with bikes with
    A. big front wheels
    B. five pedals
    C. small seats

_____ **6.** In England people made a bike with
    A. two wheels of the same size
    B. three wheels on the back
    C. no handles

_____ **7.** The new bike's back wheel turned with a
    A. chain
    B. brake
    C. pedal

_____ **8.** The safety bike became a model for
    A. model trains
    B. new cars
    C. today's bikes

Working Worms

Many people think that silk is the finest cloth of all. Just touching silk can be a surprise because it is so soft. Even more surprising is the fact that silk is made by special worms.

If you visited a silk farm, you would see two things: worms and trees. Silkworms eat only the leaves of mulberry trees. So rows and rows of these trees grow on silk farms. On some farms the leaves are picked by hand. Workers gather leaves from whole branches at once. In other places machines do this work. The farmers chop the leaves. Then they feed them to their worms.

_____ **1.** Silk is a type of very fine
  A. worm
  B. tree
  C. cloth

_____ **2.** At a silk farm, there are worms and
  A. spiders
  B. cows
  C. trees

_____ **3.** Silkworms eat only
  A. silk cloth
  B. mulberry leaves
  C. apple trees

_____ **4.** On some farms the leaves are
  A. picked by hand
  B. cooked in pots
  C. left on trees

Steck-Vaughn • Comprehension Skills Series

Silkworms do nothing but sleep and eat. They grow very quickly. In just four weeks, they grow seventy times bigger. As the worms grow, they shed their skin four times. The old skin splits and falls off.

After so much work, the worms are ready to change into moths. Each worm spins a single long thread around and around itself. This new home is called a cocoon. The thread of each cocoon is as thin as a spider's web. The farmers steam and dry the cocoons. Then the dry cocoons go to a silk-making plant. There the threads are spun into silk yarn. The yarn will be made into soft cloth that feels like a cloud.

_____ **5.** A silkworm grows
    A. slowly
    B. smaller
    C. quickly

_____ **6.** A silkworm's skin splits and
    A. gets smaller
    B. comes off
    C. becomes wet

_____ **7.** The thread of each cocoon is
    A. thin
    B. fat
    C. red

_____ **8.** Silk cloth is very
    A. rough
    B. tight
    C. soft

Hippos

Hippos are animals that live in Africa. Their name means "river horse." But they do not look very much like horses. Hippos have large, round bodies. They have short legs and small ears. They look more like pigs than horses. In fact, hippos and pigs are in the same animal group.

Like pigs, hippos love mud. They stay cool under the hot sun by rolling in mud and swimming in rivers. In spite of their great size, hippos can swim fast. A hippo's eyes and nose stay above the water as it swims. If it dives under the water, it can stay there for as long as five minutes.

_____ **1.** A hippo's name means
    A. mud roller
    B. big diver
    C. river horse

_____ **2.** Hippos have
    A. no ears
    B. small ears
    C. big ears

_____ **3.** Hippos roll in mud to
    A. go to sleep
    B. stay cool
    C. get dirty

_____ **4.** A hippo can stay underwater for
    A. five minutes
    B. one day
    C. five hours

A baby hippo can run and swim when it is born. It can get milk from its mother underwater. Baby hippos stay with their mothers for years. A baby hippo is called a calf. It begins to eat grass when it is about six months old.

Baby hippos love to play. They dive in the river and blow water from their noses. Sometimes they swim on top of their parents' backs or heads. But they cannot do this when they are grown. Grown hippos weigh as much as four tons.

_____ **5.** A baby hippo can
    A. fly
    B. talk
    C. swim

_____ **6.** Baby hippos stay with their mothers for
    A. months
    B. years
    C. weeks

_____ **7.** Baby hippos begin to eat grass when they
    A. are sleeping
    B. are born
    C. are about six months old

_____ **8.** Grown hippos can weigh up to
    A. four pounds
    B. four tons
    C. ten tons

U N I T
22 Tears and More Tears

Sometimes people cry when they are sad. Other times people cry tears of joy. But your eyes make tears all the time, whether you are crying or not. Did you know that tears help keep your eyes healthy? They keep your eyes from drying out. A special area of the eye drips all the time. It keeps the eye damp.

If you look in a mirror, you can see tiny holes in the corners of your eyes. Each hole leads to a small tube that runs to your nose. Tears run slowly into this tube drip by drip. Day and night the holes drain the tears away. If they didn't, you would always look as if you were crying!

_____

_____ **1.** Your eyes make tears
    A. all the time
    B. only at night
    C. only when you are sad

_____ **2.** Tears keep your eyes from
    A. blinking
    B. drying out
    C. opening

_____ **3.** In the corners of your eyes, there are
    A. short brushes
    B. small hairs
    C. tiny holes

_____ **4.** Each hole leads to
    A. another hole
    B. your ear
    C. a tube

If you begin to cry, there are many more tears. The holes can't drain all of them. The extra tears spill out onto your face.

Tears help keep your eyes safe. If there is something harmful in the air, the eyes fill with tears. These tears coat your eyes. They keep the harmful air out.

Contact lenses can make the eyes too dry. Some people have to add tears to their eyes. They buy bottles of eye drops to keep their eyes damp.

_____ **5.** When you cry, there are many more
  A. tears
  B. holes
  C. drains

_____ **6.** If there are harmful things in the air,
  A. the eyes will fill with tears
  B. you will never know it
  C. most people close their eyes

_____ **7.** Tears will·
  A. coat your eyes
  B. put you to sleep
  C. open your eyes

_____ **8.** Contact lenses can make the eyes too
  A. weak
  B. old
  C. dry

Cliff Swallows

Cliff swallows are special birds. They live in nests made of mud. They build their nests on the sides of cliffs. Thousands of the nests hang close together. They look like small mud cities.

Each day the swallows leave home to find insects to eat. But sometimes a bird has bad luck. Then it might still be hungry when it goes back to its nest. Swallows know just what to do when this happens. As they go home, they watch to see which neighbor had better luck. The next day they will follow this lucky friend to a fine meal.

_____ **1.** Swallows build their homes
  A. on the sides of cliffs
  B. up in the trees
  C. out of grass and sticks

_____ **2.** Swallow nests look like
  A. strange birds
  B. mud cities
  C. new hotels

_____ **3.** Swallows eat
  A. flowers
  B. mud
  C. insects

_____ **4.** To find food a swallow might follow
  A. another swallow
  B. hungry animals
  C. a road

Swallows have ways to solve other problems, too. Sometimes a swallow will pick up one of its eggs with its mouth. Then it will place the egg in a neighbor's nest. When the baby bird hatches, the neighbor bird will be its mother.

No one knows why swallows do this. Maybe these birds are trying to get other birds to do their work. Birds called cowbirds do that. They lay their eggs in other birds' nests. But some people have another idea. They think that the swallows may be moving their eggs to a safer place.

_____ **5.** Swallows have ways to
    A. solve their problems
    B. eat small snakes
    C. walk on water

_____ **6.** A swallow can pick up an egg with its
    A. feet
    B. mouth
    C. wings

_____ **7.** Swallows will sometimes put an egg in
    A. a cave
    B. another nest
    C. a river

_____ **8.** Cowbirds try to get other birds to
    A. fall from their nests
    B. live with them
    C. do their work

Visiting Caves

Some caves are open for visitors. Guides take people down stairs that go into the caves. Then they guide people on paths under the ground. The paths are paved and lighted. As the people walk through, the guides tell how the caves were formed.

Some people would rather see a wild cave. Wild caves do not have stairs, lights, or paved trails. People who know how to go into wild caves are called cavers. They take classes to learn how to go through the caves safely. Wild caves can be very dangerous. Some parts may be underwater. Other parts may have very low roofs. Cavers may have to crawl to get through these tight places.

_____ **1.** Caves that are open for visitors have
    A. lights and paths
    B. very low roofs
    C. no stairs

_____ **2.** The tour guides tell how the caves were
    A. paved
    B. formed
    C. opened

_____ **3.** People who go into wild caves are called
    A. miners
    B. riders
    C. cavers

_____ **4.** Wild caves can be
    A. tight
    B. paved
    C. lighted

Steck-Vaughn • Comprehension Skills Series

At Carlsbad Caverns people can go into a cave that is almost wild. It is called a new cave. There are stairs at the start. But there are no bright lights or paved paths. People take their own flashlights. They follow a guide along paths marked with red tape.

Going into a quiet, dark cave can be fun. Long rocks hang from the roof of the cave. Other rocks shoot up from the cave's floor like tall buildings. Dripping water makes the rocks shine. Sounds bounce off the walls and echo again and again. With no light in the cave, you can see what total darkness is like. A cave is really an exciting place!

_____ **5.** A new cave is
    A. almost wild
    B. above ground
    C. very small

_____ **6.** In a new cave, people take their own
    A. ropes
    B. stairs
    C. flashlights

_____ **7.** Some of the rocks in caves are like
    A. tall buildings
    B. cold pools
    C. shaky stairs

_____ **8.** Dripping water makes the rocks
    A. crack
    B. shine
    C. melt

The Name Game

Years ago in England, people had only one name. Each name had a special meaning. A baby might be given a name that meant "brave" or "bright." The parents hoped that the child would live up to the name. They thought that a good name would help the child.

Then towns got larger. Sometimes people with the same name lived close to one another. Their friends had to have a way to tell them apart. So people began to have longer names. The new names told something about the person.

_____ **1.** Years ago people had only one
  A. hat
  B. baby
  C. name

_____ **2.** Each name had
  A. a special meaning
  B. the same letters
  C. one correct spelling

_____ **3.** Sometimes people had
  A. too many names
  B. the same name
  C. two towns

_____ **4.** The new names told about the
  A. parents
  B. town
  C. person

Sometimes the names told where a person lived. If there were two Johns, one might have been called John of the Woods. Maybe the other John had red hair. He would have been called John the Red.

By about the year 1300, most people had two names. They also started to give their names to their children. Many of these last names are still used today. Lincoln was a town in England. *Johnson* meant "son of John." Smiths were workers who used hammers. They worked with metal, wood, or stone.

_____ **5.** John the Red had
   A. red hair
   B. brown eyes
   C. black teeth

_____ **6.** By about 1300, people gave their children
   A. their own rooms
   B. more money
   C. two names

_____ **7.** Lincoln was a
   A. road
   B. town
   C. mountain

_____ **8.** Smiths worked with
   A. saws
   B. hammers
   C. knives

Writing

Read the story below. Think about the facts. Then answer the questions in complete sentences.

At age 39, Franklin Roosevelt got polio. It harmed his muscles. He could not move his back, arms, or legs. People thought he could not work. His mother told him to quit. But he did not.

For many months Roosevelt exercised hard. In time he was able to use his hands. Soon he could move his back, too. He tried to walk again. He could do it with leg braces or someone's help. He did not let polio end his life or work. Roosevelt went on to become President of the United States.

1. What did polio do to Roosevelt's muscles?

_____

_____

2. What did Roosevelt do to fight polio?

_____

_____

3. What job did Roosevelt go on to have?

_____

_____

To check your answers, turn to page 60.

Prewriting

Think of an idea you might write about, such as a person you admire or a game you played. Write the idea in the center of the idea web below. Then fill out the rest of the web with facts.

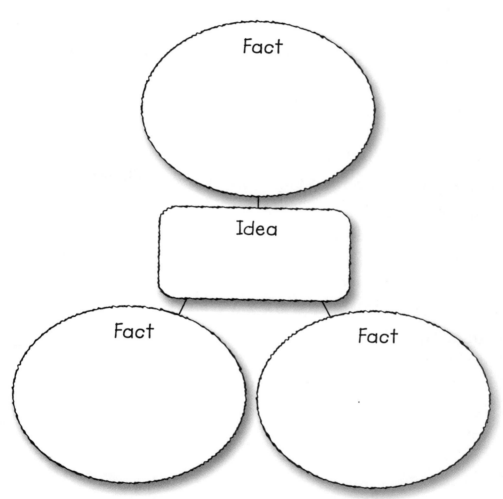

On Your Own

Now use another sheet of paper to write a story about your idea. Use the facts from your idea web.

To check your answers, turn to page 60.

Check Yourself

Practice Finding Facts, Page 4

2. C

To check your answers to pages 6–29, see page 61.

Writing, Page 30

Possible answers include:

1. Humans have traveled there and brought back soil to study.
2. The soil is made of rock and glass.
3. Each glass bit is about as small as a period.

Writing, Page 31

Check that you have three facts in your story.

To check your answers to pages 32–57, see page 62.

Writing, Page 58

Possible answers include:

1. It harmed them. He could not move his back, legs, or arms.
2. He exercised hard for many months.
3. He became President of the United States.

Writing, Page 59

Check that you have three facts in your story.

Check Yourself

Unit 1	Unit 2	Unit 3	Unit 4	Unit 5	Unit 6	Unit 7	Unit 8	Unit 9	Unit 10	Unit 11	Unit 12
pp. 6–7	pp. 8–9	pp. 10–11	pp. 12–13	pp. 14–15	pp. 16–17	pp. 18–19	pp. 20–21	pp. 22–23	pp. 24–25	pp. 26–27	pp. 28–29
1. B	1. A	1. B	1. B	1. B	1. A	1. C	1. C	1. B	1. A	1. C	1. B
2. A	2. B	2. C	2. A	2. C	2. C	2. B	2. A	2. A	2. C	2. A	2. A
3. C	3. B	3. B	3. C	3. C	3. C	3. B	3. A	3. A	3. A	3. C	3. B
4. B	4. C	4. B	4. B	4. B	4. C	4. A	4. B	4. B	4. A	4. B	4. B
5. A	5. A	5. A	5. A	5. A	5. A	5. C	5. B	5. C	5. C	5. B	5. C
6. B	6. B	6. B	6. C	6. C	6. C	6. C	6. A	6. B	6. C	6. A	6. A
7. A	7. A	7. B	7. C	7. C	7. B	7. A	7. C	7. B	7. B	7. B	7. B
8. C	8. C	8. A	8. C	8. A	8. A	8. C	8. B	8. C	8. A	8. A	8. A

Unit 13 pp. 32–33	Unit 14 pp. 34–35	Unit 15 pp. 36–37	Unit 16 pp. 38–39	Unit 17 pp. 40–41	Unit 18 pp. 42–43	Unit 19 pp. 44–45	Unit 20 pp. 46–47	Unit 21 pp. 48–49	Unit 22 pp. 50–51	Unit 23 pp. 52–53	Unit 24 pp. 54–55	Unit 25 pp. 56–57
1. C	1. B	1. C	1. C	1. B	1. C	1. C	1. C	1. C	1. A	1. A	1. A	1. C
2. B	2. A	2. C	2. A	2. C	2. C	2. A	2. C	2. B	2. B	2. B	2. B	2. A
3. B	3. A	3. C	3. C	3. B	3. A	3. B	3. B	3. B	3. C	3. C	3. C	3. B
4. A	4. C	4. B	4. A	4. A	4. C	4. B	4. A	4. A	4. C	4. A	4. A	4. C
5. C	5. A	5. A	5. B	5. C	5. B	5. A	5. C	5. C	5. A	5. A	5. A	5. A
6. A	6. C	6. C	6. B	6. A	6. C	6. A	6. B	6. B	6. A	6. B	6. C	6. C
7. C	7. B	7. B	7. A	7. B	7. C	7. A	7. A	7. C	7. A	7. B	7. A	7. B
8. B	8. A	8. A	8. C	8. C	8. A	8. C	8. C	8. B	8. C	8. C	8. B	8. B